When Light Strikes

Contents

Adapted by Benjamin Hulme-Cross

Hiccup   Chief Stoick   Toothless   Mildew   Astrid

Chapter One

The Vikings and the dragons usually lived peacefully together. Recently though, the dragons had been causing a lot of damage in the village. They kept landing on the houses and breaking them! They didn't mean to – but it was still very annoying for the Vikings.

Then Hiccup, the chief's son, had a brilliant idea – the Vikings could build huge perches for the dragons, so that they wouldn't have to land on the houses!

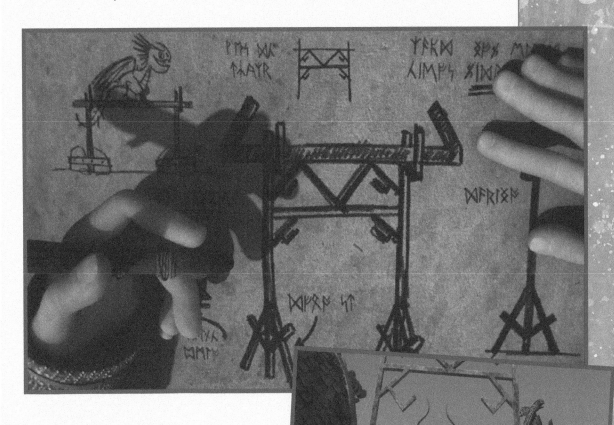

Hiccup and his friends found some big metal posts, and started making the perches at once.

At dinner that night, Hiccup was very excited. "These perches are just the beginning," he said. "Next, we'll make landing areas for the dragons – and maybe even some stables in the caves."

Hiccup's father, Chief Stoick, chuckled. "Hold on now, son, we have to put Vikings before dragons!" he said.

Outside, thunder rumbled. Hiccup's dragon, Toothless, was restless. Toothless was a Night Fury, one of the most feared of all dragons. Toothless had been injured a long time ago, and Hiccup had built him a new tail fin. They had been best friends ever since.

There was a second roll of thunder, and Toothless dashed outside. Hiccup, Stoick, and the chief's friend, Gobber, looked out from the doorway. Massive bolts of lightning flashed down, setting fire to houses all over the village.

"I've never seen so much lightning!" said Stoick. "Thor must be very angry!" The Vikings believed that the god Thor threw lightning at Vikings if he was cross with them.

A group of Vikings had gathered outside Stoick's house, and they were very scared. They watched as Toothless leapt around the village. The lightning bolts seemed to be chasing him from one perch to another.

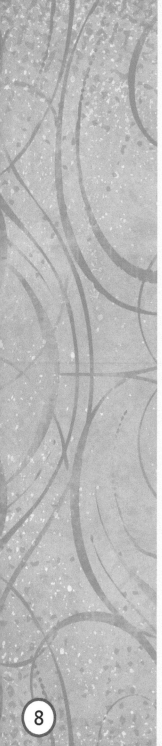

After a little while, an angry Viking called Mildew stepped forward. He was famous for hating dragons.

"Can't you see what's happening?" he asked. "That dragon is a Night Fury and a Night Fury is the child of lightning and death! Thor has sent all this lightning to punish us for having a Night Fury in the village. The only way to stop the lightning is to get rid of that dragon!"

Chapter Two

The next day the weather was better. Hiccup was desperate to prove the lightning wasn't Toothless's fault, so he came up with a plan.

Hiccup and his friends decided to build a large metal statue of Thor. Perhaps that would make the god happy again, so there would be no more lightning. Then no one could blame anything on Toothless!

The friends set to work making parts of Thor out of metal, and then they welded the parts together into one huge statue.

The villagers gasped and then cheered when they saw the amazing statue Hiccup and his friends had made.

"Well done, my boy!" said Stoick proudly. "Now Thor will smile on us again."

"Fools!" growled Mildew. "A statue won't make any difference! It's the Night Fury that Thor's worried about!"

Later that night another storm hit the village. The Vikings watched in terror as lightning struck the statue of Thor himself! It started a big fire, which damaged even more buildings.

"It doesn't look as though this statue is what Thor wanted," said Stoick sadly.

"Of course it isn't!" Mildew yelled. "We have to get rid of the Night Fury!" A large crowd of Vikings agreed with Mildew. Things began to look very bad for Toothless.

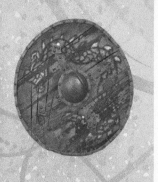

Quietly, Stoick told Hiccup to take Toothless away and hide somewhere safe, far from the village. Hiccup had been thinking just the same thing. While an angry mob of Vikings searched the village from top to bottom, Hiccup and Toothless quietly flew away.

Chapter Three

The boy and the dragon flew sadly through the wind and rain.

"We have to get as far away as possible," said Hiccup. "Every moment counts. They'll send out a search party to try and catch you."

Toothless flew on as fast as he could, but the storm was making things difficult.

All of a sudden, a bolt of lightning hit the tail fin that Hiccup had built for Toothless. Toothless swerved and fell towards the forest below. Together, Toothless and Hiccup crashed through the branches and landed in a tangled heap on the forest floor.

Hiccup stood up. "We can't stay here, Toothless," he said. "I don't think we're far enough away from the village." Toothless groaned, and Hiccup noticed that the lightning had burned away most of his tail fin.

"Wait a minute," said Hiccup. "The lightning hit your tail fin, and it's made of metal, just like the statue and the new perches in the village ..."

Before Hiccup could say any more, an angry crowd of villagers ran out of the trees and surrounded them. Moments later they had captured Toothless and tied him to a huge wooden cart.

"Say goodbye to the Night Fury, Hiccup!" said Mildew, with a nasty grin on his face. Hiccup stood by, shocked and helpless, as the villagers hauled Toothless away on the cart.

Chapter Four

Back at the village, Stoick was standing on a jetty in the harbour. Behind him on the jetty was Toothless, still strapped to the cart. In front of him stood Mildew and the crowd of angry Vikings who had caught Toothless.

"I know you're scared," said Stoick to the crowd. "But this is not the way we Vikings do things. Dragons are our friends, and so we're going to let Toothless go."

"You've gone mad, Stoick!" Mildew snarled. "We have to get rid of that Night Fury, or Thor will carry on sending lightning to punish us!"

Just then, Hiccup appeared. He had walked all the way back from the forest.

"Quick!" said Hiccup's friend Astrid when she saw him. "You've got to do something. They're going to float Toothless out to sea!"

It looked as if Mildew and the villagers were about to attack Stoick to get to Toothless. Hiccup ran forward.

"Stop!" he shouted. "The lightning has nothing to do with Toothless! I can prove it." He snatched up a metal spear and leapt onto the back of Astrid's dragon. "It's because of the metal. The lightning keeps striking metal!"

"This is ridiculous!" Mildew yelled. "We need to get rid of the Night Fury!"

Everyone was watching Hiccup though, as Astrid flew him up to the top of a ship's mast.

"Watch!" he called out. "When I attach the metal spear to this mast, the lightning will ..." Suddenly, before he could finish what he was saying, a bolt of lightning flashed down and struck the spear in his hand.

The lightning passed right through Hiccup's body and knocked him off the mast. Slowly he toppled backwards and fell down into the water below.

Toothless saw what had happened. He tore himself free from the cart and dived after Hiccup.

Chapter Five

The next morning, Hiccup sat up in bed. "What happened?" he groaned.

"A lightning bolt struck you on the head!" said Stoick proudly. "And Toothless rescued you from drowning."

"Now does everyone believe me? They must know it was the metal in the statue and the perches that was attracting the lightning! They don't blame Toothless any more, do they?"

"Don't worry, son," said Stoick. "Toothless is safe here. After seeing what you went through last night, everyone understands." said Stoick. "Especially Mildew. We put the statue of Thor just outside his front door!"

SOUND
ADVICE

ALLSORTED.

An exclusive edition for

for all your gift books and gift stationery

This edition first published in Great Britain in 2017
by Allsorted Ltd, Watford, Herts, UK WD19 4BG

Author: Roffy
Cover design: Milestone Creative
Contents layout: seagulls.net

ISBN: 978-1-910562-94-9

Printed in China

CONTENTS

INTRODUCTION

We've all seen the poster. There's a picture of a cute little kitten clinging to a washing line and below is the phrase 'Just hang on'.

Did that poster do the trick? Were you and everyone you know forever encouraged by looking at a poor, innocent creature that had been suspended over a barrel of hungry crocodiles by a sadistic photographer?

OK, there may not have been any crocodiles, but you get the point – a single one-liner is not enough to help out everyone in every situation.

Instead you need a whole new ABC – advice, banter and counsel. A collection of one-liners that show you understand the way the world works and how to live with it, deal with it or move on.

Some of the one-liners may appear a bit cynical, but if delivered with a smile, you can still give someone a lift. And if delivered with a hug, you might also get their wallet.

LESSONS IN LOVE

SOME PEOPLE ARE LUCKY ENOUGH
TO MEET THEIR ONE TRUE LOVE
WHEN THEY ARE YOUNG. THEY HAVE
A WHIRLWIND ROMANCE, MARRY
AND LIVE HAPPILY TOGETHER.

Those people also tend to be fictional. Thankfully, in most films in which they appear, they become the unwitting victims of a haunted house or brain-hungry zombies.

Back in the real world, finding 'the one' may feel like an impossible task. It's not easy meeting someone and getting to know them. It can be even harder to let them go if it's not working out.

Along the way, the right one-liner may not mend a broken heart, but it can show you've been there, you care and you understand. And at least it can help kick-start a conversation over a consolation pint of beer/ice-cream/vodka.

MR OR MRS RIGHT

THEY ARE OUT THERE. SOMEWHERE.

- Every pot has a lid.

- Someone is looking for exactly what you have to offer.

- Love at first sight is impossible if the only thing you look at is your phone.

- One day someone will come into your life and you'll know why it never worked out with anyone else.

- The minute you settle for less than you deserve, you get even less than you settled for.

- Make happy those who are near, and those who are far will come.

- One day you will meet the perfect person who will want absolutely nothing to do with you.

- Take away the looks, money and success and there's no difference between you and Johnny Depp.

- You have to kiss a lot of frogs before you find a prince.

- Men are from earth, women are from earth. Get over it.

THEY SAY THAT THE RIGHT PERSON WILL ARRIVE IN YOUR LIFE ONE DAY. YOURS JUST HASN'T LEARNT HOW TO USE GOOGLE MAPS YET.

PLENTY MORE

THERE ARE FEWER FISH IN THE SEA THESE DAYS SO WE NEED SOME ALTERNATIVE. THERE ARE PLENTY MORE:

- prawns on the barbecue.

- lefts to swipe.

- sesame seeds on the bun.

- spoons in the cutlery drawer.

- Pokemon on the Go.

- beans in the tin.

- tomatoes on the vine.

- apps in the store.

- pints in the keg.

- shots in the bottle.

- feathers in the pillow.

- cows in the field.

- monkeys in the zoo.

TROUBLE IN PARADISE

SORRY TO HEAR IT'S NOT WORKING OUT.

- It's a fact of life that everyone seems normal until you get to know them.

- It's time to choose between turning the page and closing the book.

- The question isn't why someone keeps hurting you, it's why you keep letting them.

- If you ever find yourself in the wrong story, it's fine to write yourself out of it.

- Buy a stethoscope and listen to your heart.

- Can't figure out where you stand with someone? It's time to stop standing and start walking.

IT'S OVER

WHEN ENDING IS BETTER THAN PENDING.

- There's no point in worrying about someone that isn't worried about you.

- Sometimes the person you want most is the person you are better off without.

- You won't find the right one if you don't let the wrong one go.

- If they hurt you, cry a river and then drown them in it.

- Love gone wrong is often life gone right.

- If they are stupid enough to walk away, be smart enough to let them go.

- I'm sorry your relationship with the freakshow that everyone warned you about didn't work out.

IT'S STILL OVER

DON'T MAKE THE SAME MISTAKE TWICE.

- Don't go back to your ex. It's like reading the same book again when you know how the story ends.

- Not all exes are annoying. Some are dead.

- Break-ups aren't always meant for make-ups – sometimes they are meant for wake-ups.

- Relationships are like algebra. It's fine to look at your X and wonder Y.

- Taking your ex back is like going to a car boot sale and buying back your own crap.

- Remember that person you couldn't live without? Well, look at you living!

ITCHING TO HITCH

BECAUSE MARRIAGE ISN'T ALL IT'S CRACKED UP TO BE.

- Marriage has its surprises, but it's largely asking each other 'Do you have to do that right now?'.

- Top three situations that require witnesses:
1) Crimes 2) Accidents 3) Marriages.

- You want to know what it's like to be married? Leave me alone. Hey, why are you ignoring me?

- Marriages are made in heaven. Just like thunder and lightning.

- Indecision is the key to flexibility.

- Love may be blind but marriage is a real eye-opener.

DOS AND DON'TS

THE FIRST RULE OF RELATIONSHIPS? DON'T ASK ME...

- Avoid arguments about the toilet seat. Use the sink.

- Laugh and the world laughs with you. Snore and you sleep alone.

- Never break someone's heart because they have only one. Break their bones because they have 206 of them.

- Never wrestle with a pig. You both get dirty and the pig likes it.

- Nobody will ever win the battle of the sexes. There's too much fraternising with the enemy.

- See no evil, hear no evil, date no evil.

- The hardest part of getting their phone number is working up the courage to go through their bin to find it.

WHAT IS LOVE?

SOME DEFINITIONS YOU WON'T FIND IN A DICTIONARY.

- The difference between true love and dinosaurs: we're sure that dinosaurs once existed on this earth.

- Love is like a roller coaster: when it's good you don't want to get off, and when it isn't... you can't wait to throw up.

- Love is a rare gem that needs to be polished, praised and pampered, every day.

- Love because you are willing to accept the risk, not because it's safe or certain.

- Remember, if you smoke after sex you're doing it too fast.

- You can't buy love, but you pay heavily for it.

- Sex is like air; it's not important unless you aren't getting any.

- There's a fine line between cuddling and holding someone down so they can't get away.

IT COULD BE WORSE

IF YOU THINK YOUR LOVE LIFE IS BAD, TAKE A LOOK AT MINE.

- Alcohol won't mend a broken heart. But that doesn't mean I won't try it again tonight.
- After a few more blind dates I'll get a free dog.
- I flirted with disaster last night. Now disaster is stalking me on Facebook.
- I'm in a long-distance relationship – my partner is in the future.
- I've spent the past four years looking for my ex's killer, but no one will do it.

BATTLE OF THE SEXES – MEN

DING DING, ROUND 1.

- What might look like a knight in shining armour is just an idiot in tin foil.
- All men are animals, but some make better pets.

- Women can fake orgasms. Men can fake a whole relationship.

- A real Don Juan has to dress not only tastefully but also very quickly.

- Men are like mascara – they run at the first sign of emotion.

- Never try to drown your troubles. Especially if he can swim.

BATTLE OF THE SEXES – WOMEN

DING DING, ROUND 2.

- Why do women always ask questions that have no right answers?

- Women are like roads. The more curves they have, the more the dangerous they are.

- Women can be satisfied with 3.5 inches. It doesn't matter if it's Visa or Mastercard.

- Telling a girl to calm down works about as well as trying to baptise a cat.

- There are two theories to arguing with women. Neither one works.

FRIENDS, FAMILY AND FOOLS

THE STORY OF OUR LIFE IS SHAPED BY THE PEOPLE IN IT. FAMILY AND FRIENDS PLAY THE LEADING ROLES THROUGHOUT AND OTHER FOLKS PERFORM BRIEF BUT IMPORTANT BIT-PARTS. IT'S POSSIBLE TO GET A CAMEO FROM A HOLLYWOOD A-LISTER, BUT THEY MIGHT DEMAND A MASSIVE TRAILER AND FREE BLUE M&MS FOR THEIR ENTOURAGE, SO ON BALANCE THEY'RE BEST AVOIDED.

All of the real characters can be a source of joy or frustration. And the longer we know them, the more likely they are to be a source of both – the skilled ones somehow both at the same time. How do they do that?

Knowing that everyone is different is the first step to understanding why your story is the way it is. Keeping those people happy might guide you to your own happy ending. Either way, don't count on a sequel.

FRIENDS LIKE THESE

FRIENDSHIP SHOULDN'T COME WITH A PRICE TAG.

- You don't use and throw away a real friend. You use them again and again.

- At least hermits have no peer pressure.

- If you lend someone £50 and never see that person again, it was probably worth it.

- True friendship comes when the silence between two people is comfortable.

- With true friends... even water drunk together is sweet enough.

- A friend to everybody is a friend to nobody.

- You are such a good friend that if we were on a sinking ship together and there was only one life jacket, I'd miss you heaps and think of you often.

- Real friends are the ones who survive the transition to a new phone.

FAMILY MATTERS

AT LEAST YOU CAN PICK YOUR FRIENDS.

- Even when you hate them, they still love you.

- Happiness is having a large, loving, caring, close-knit family in another city.

- Everyone's family tree produces some lemons, some nuts and a few bad apples.

- Unfortunately the gene pool has no lifeguard.

- Families are like fudge – mostly sweet with a few nuts.

- Our parents were never our age.

ANKLE BITERS

THE CHIP OFF THE OLD BLOCK CAN BECOME A SPLINTER.

- Life is tough enough without having someone kick you from the inside.

- Be nice to your kids. They'll choose your nursing home.

- Parents who are afraid to put their foot down usually have children who step on their toes.

- By the time a man realises that his father was right, he has a son who thinks he's wrong.

- You spend the first two years of their life encouraging them to walk and talk. Then you spend the rest of your life telling them to sit down and shut up.

- One generation plants the trees, and another gets the shade.

- Grandchildren and grandparents get along so well because they have a common enemy.

- If you have a headache, do what it says on the aspirin bottle: take two, and keep away from children.

- The sole purpose of a child's middle name is so they can tell when they're really in trouble.

- Having one child makes you a parent; having two makes you a referee.

CRITICS

NO MATTER HOW WELL YOU HAVE DONE, THERE'S ALWAYS ONE.

- You did a great job – everyone else can see that.

- Life is like photography, you use the negatives to develop.

- For every action there is an equal and opposite criticism.

- No good deed goes unpunished.

- People tend to make rules for others and exceptions for themselves.

- A cynic's work is never done.

- Before you criticise someone, you should walk a mile in their shoes. That way, when you criticise them, you're a mile away and you have their shoes.

LOUDMOUTHS

SOMETIMES WE'RE STUCK WITH SOMEONE WITH NO VOLUME CONTROL. OR TACT CONTROL.

- Empty vessels make most noise.

- Generally speaking, they aren't learning much if their mouth is moving.

- Light travels faster than sound. This is why some people appear bright until you hear them speak.

- There are two kinds of people who don't say much: those who are quiet and those who talk a lot.

- Silence is golden but duct tape is silver.

- A closed mouth gathers no foot.

- Anything is possible if you don't know what you're talking about.

- Better to remain silent and be thought a fool, than to speak and remove all doubt.

- One nice thing about egotists: they don't talk about other people.

TROLLS

EVEN PEOPLE YOU DON'T MEET IN REAL LIFE CAN BE TROUBLE.

- Those who throw dirt only lose ground.

- Don't let people drive you crazy when you know it's within walking distance.

- Perhaps they went for a pat on the back, missed, and gave you a kick in the ass instead.

- Haters are like crickets: they chirp all day and when you walk by them they shut up.

- No matter what happens, somebody will find a way to take it too seriously.

- He who laughs last thinks slowest.

EVERYDAY IDIOTS

EXACTLY WHO DOES SUFFER FOOLS GLADLY?

- Wise people think all they say, fools say all they think.

- Some drink at the fountain of knowledge. Others just gargle.

- When it comes to thought, some people stop at nothing.

- Even a numpty can bring a smile to your face, when pushed down the stairs.

- It is said that if you line up all the cars in the world end to end, someone would be stupid enough to try and overtake them.

- Make it idiot-proof and someone will make a better idiot.

- Never underestimate the power of stupid people in large groups.

- Some people are only alive because it's illegal to shoot them.

- Everyone has a photographic memory. Some don't have film.

- Some cause happiness wherever they go. Others whenever they go.

EVERYONE CAN BE A FOOL FOR FIVE MINUTES A DAY; WISDOM CONSISTS OF NOT EXCEEDING THE LIMIT.

GENIUS DOES WHAT IT MUST, TALENT DOES WHAT IT CAN, AND YOU HAD BEST DO WHAT YOU'RE TOLD.

MOVING ON

WHEN IT'S TIME TO FORGIVE AND FORGET. OR NOT.

- Always forgive your enemies – nothing annoys them so much.

- Forgive your enemies but never forget their names.

- Forgiveness is giving up the hope that the past could have been any different.

- To forgive is to set a prisoner free and discover that the prisoner was you.

- Friends may come and go, but enemies tend to accumulate.

- Sometimes the first step to forgiveness is realising the other person was born an idiot.

- Don't regret burning bridges. Regret that certain people weren't on them when you burnt them.

- Never hit a man with glasses. Hit him with a baseball bat.

GET PRACTICAL

A LITTLE LESS CONVERSATION, A LITTLE MORE ACTION PLEASE.

- If you can't convince them, confuse them.

- Never go to bed angry – stay awake and plot your revenge.

- If someone hates you for no reason, give them a reason.

- An extremely positive outlook won't solve all your problems, but it will annoy enough people to make it worth a shot.

- If someone cuts you up at the lights, turn the other cheek. Everyone understands a mooning.

- If you feel stressed out, make yourself a nice hot cup of tea. Then pour it in the lap of whoever stressed you out in the first place.

- In the past, when you were angry with someone you fought them. Now you just unfriend them on Facebook.

- Here's a stress ball. Throw it at the last person who pissed you off.

- Sometimes the best helping hand you can give is a firm push over a cliff.

JUDGE MENTAL

EVERYONE HAS AN OPINION.

- Care less, smile more.

- You wouldn't worry so much about what people thought of you if you knew how rarely they did.

- Not worrying about what other people think is one of the best decisions you will ever make.

- The unhappiest people in the world are those who care the most what other people think.

- People are going to judge you anyway, so forget everyone and just be yourself.

- Doubt kills more dreams than failure ever will.

- Fake people have an image to maintain. Real people just don't care.

- A tiger doesn't lose sleep over the opinion of a sheep.

- Screw them – have fun and give them something to talk about.

EVERYONE ELSE

WHEN YOU JUST HAVE TO GRIN AND BEAR THEM.

- One day we might live in a world where people come with on/off switches.

- If you think there is good in everybody, then you haven't met everybody.

- Trying to understand some people is like trying to smell the number 9.

- Discretion is being able to raise your eyebrow instead of your voice.

- Some people create their own storms and then get upset when it rains.

- At least being pissed off is better than being pissed on.

- There's no need for revenge. Just sit back and wait. Eventually they will screw up, and, if you're lucky, you'll be able to watch.

WORKING IT

THE TYPICAL WORKING WEEK IN THE UK
IS 36.3 HOURS. IF YOU ENJOY YOUR JOB,
THAT'S THE IDEAL AMOUNT. IF YOU DON'T,
EVERY ONE OF THOSE HOURS SEEMS TO
LAST FOR 178 MINUTES OR MORE.

Nevertheless, work always has its ups and downs: sometimes a fun challenge, sometimes a bit slow and boring, sometimes a bit fired and looking for another job.

It's the people that we meet through work that are often what make it worthwhile. They can be inspiring by their example, or a warning about why it's not always the best idea to stay in the same job for too long.

And if they are lucky enough to meet you, you should be armed with the right one-liner to help them know their place, pick up the pace or not leave a trace...

A RECENT POLL SHOWED THAT 70% OF PEOPLE ARE UNHAPPY WITH THEIR CURRENT JOB. THE OTHER 30% ARE UNEMPLOYED.

BETWEEN JOBS

GETTING A JOB IS HARD WORK IN ITSELF.

- Somewhere there is a toolbox missing the right tool.

- The right job is only the right interview away.

- Make sure your CV is not a list of things you hope you are never asked to do.

- You'd better get a job before you have an out of money experience.

- Refuse to leave the interview unless you are hired.

- There's an opening for you somewhere. Though it might be a door.

- If you're worried, ask the interviewer for a copy of their CV to confirm that they possess the qualifications to interview you.

- At least your mornings are your own.

- Be careful your digital footprint does not stamp all over your job prospects.

DAY ONE

ADVICE FOR THE NEW STARTER.

- Keep your boss's boss off your boss's back.

- Don't present a problem without a solution.

- You can go anywhere you want if you look serious and carry a clipboard.

- How long have I been working for this company? Ever since they threatened to fire me.

- No one trusts anyone who carries too many pens or keys.

- Use artificial sweetener at work – add it to everything you say to your boss.

- While there is no I in 'team', try not to be the big A.

- There's two ways to get things done: the right way and the drunk way.

- Three correct guesses in a row and you too can be an expert.

ON THE
BRIGHT SIDE

SAY 'NO' TO BEING NEGATIVE.

- If you don't know what it is, call it an 'issue'.

- If you don't know how it works, say it needs a 'process'.

- If you don't know whether it's worth doing, call it an 'option'.

- If you don't know how it could possibly be done call it an 'exciting opportunity'.

- If you don't know how to do something, 'empower' someone else to do it for you.

- Never criticise or boast, call it 'information sharing'.

- Never call something a failure, it's a 'positive learning experience'.

- Never argue, have an 'adult conversation'.

AIM FOR THE TOP

HOW TO GET AHEAD WITH BEING 'THAT GUY'.

- You become the average of the people you spend time with.

- Never be good at anything you don't want to do.

- Praise publicly and criticise privately.

- Don't apologise for being an expert.

- If you own your mistakes and move on, everyone else will too.

- Don't make a mess to close a sale – it will cost more to clean it up.

- If the customer is always wrong, help them to be right.

TOO BUSY
TO THINK

SOMETIMES IT CAN GET A BIT INTENSE.

- Keep calm, nobody else knows what they are doing either.

- You don't have to solve all the problems today.

- Focus on progression, not perfection.

- When you feel like quitting remember why you started.

- Take life one panic attack at a time.

- Sometimes it's OK if the only thing you did today is breathe.

- It doesn't matter what others are doing, what matters is what you are doing.

BUSY BEE

IT CAN TAKE EFFORT TO LOOK BUSY.

- Never walk anywhere without a document in your hands.

- Always have a spreadsheet open on your computer.

- A messy desk means you are too busy to tidy it.

- Keep a stack of binders on the floor near your desk.

- Divert everything to voicemail.

- A small sigh and a mournful look says a thousand words.

- Take two jackets to work. One that you use and one to leave on your chair to make it look like you are still there.

DON'T TRY TOO HARD

YOU MAKE ENEMIES BY LOOKING TOO EFFICIENT.

- Laziness is when a person doesn't fake that he's working.

- Remember, it's not what you do... it's what you get away with.

- Hard work is the refuge of people who have nothing whatever to do.

- Einstein said space and time are the same so your project is just five miles late.

- If it wasn't for the last minute, nothing would get done.

- Don't put off till tomorrow what you can get someone else to do today.

- Always give 100% at work: 12% Monday, 23% Tuesday, 40% Wednesday, 20% Thursday, 5% Friday.

- It's OK – after Tuesday, even the calendar goes WTF.

IT DOESN'T MATTER HOW MUCH YOU WORK, THERE WILL ALWAYS BE SOMEONE THAT WORKS LESS BUT EARNS MORE.

HOW IT WORKS

SURVIVE THE WORKPLACE BY KNOWING THE RULES.

- The reward for a job well done is more work.

- A committee is twelve people doing the work of one.

- A cubicle is just a padded cell without a door.

- The longer the title, the less important the job.

- If you ever forget that you got a haircut, someone will definitely point it out to you.

- Your job is secure. No one else wants it.

- Anything worth taking seriously is worth making fun of.

- It's lonely at the top, but you eat better.

- Keep your nose to the grindstone and your shoulder to the wheel... it's cheaper than plastic surgery.

- It takes patience to listen. It takes skill to pretend you're listening.

- The only people who aren't worried about losing their job are sleeping with their boss.

GOOD VIBRATIONS

A LITTLE JOY IN THE WORKPLACE CAN BE INFECTIOUS.

- Invite new starters out to lunch. Preferably the pub.

- Don't wear any underwear for a day. Carefully.

- Take turns on the music playlist or choice of radio station.

- Get everyone to tell their favourite joke. Best done when no one from HR is around.

- Get to know the employee who annoys you the most.

- Be as friendly to the cleaner as you are to the chairman of the board.

- Write to the most famous person in your industry asking for one piece of advice.

- Say 'thank you' to your clients and suppliers as often as possible.

- But please don't wear comedy ties or socks. Ever.

TECH TALK

SOME WORDS OF WISDOM FOR THE TECHNICALLY PERPLEXED.

- Successful people rarely 'reply all'.

- No one was fired for keeping separate work and personal email accounts.

- Email is not always the best way to communicate – that's why they don't use it as a fire alarm.

- A computer is almost human – except that it doesn't blame its mistakes on another computer.

- Don't email anything you wouldn't say in person – it could be forwarded to your mother.

- Change your password to 'incorrect' so whenever you forget it, the computer will say 'Your password is incorrect'.

- Behind every successful student, there is a deactivated Facebook account.

- If Bill Gates had a penny for every time you have to reboot your computer... Oh, he does.

- Be glad you are not a General if your auto-correct changes 'lunch order' to 'launch order'.

WHOOPS

**SOME CALL IT A MISTAKE,
SOME CALL IT LEARNING ON THE JOB.**

- It's not your mistake if you haven't been trained properly.

- We all make mistakes, as the hedgehog said as he climbed off the scrubbing brush.

- You do not need a parachute to skydive. You only need a parachute to skydive twice.

- Some of us learn from the mistakes of others; the rest of us have to be the others.

- Repeat the same mistake enough times and you can call it a procedure.

- When you don't know what you are doing, do it neatly.

- Remember, it's not what you do, it's what you get away with.

- To err is human, to blame it on somebody else shows management potential.

DAY BY DAY

TOP TIPS FOR THE WORKPLACE.

- Don't be irreplaceable – if you cannot be replaced, you cannot be promoted.

- Make your presentation like a mini-skirt. Long enough to cover the essentials but short enough to hold their attention.

- If at first you don't succeed, try again. Then quit. No use being a fool about it.

- Doing things that you are not supposed to do at work makes your vision, hearing and alertness so much better.

- Better to understand a little than to misunderstand a lot.

- The secret to creativity: knowing how to hide your sources.

- When confronted by a difficult problem ask yourself the question, 'How would Batman handle this?'.

SOME WORRISOME WORRIES

IT CAN HAPPEN TO ANY ONE OF US.
THAT MOMENT WHEN YOU ARE IN BED,
HAPPILY NODDING OFF AND THEN YOUR
MIND PLAYS A DIRTY TRICK ON YOU. JUST
BEFORE YOU FALL ASLEEP, YOUR BRAIN
DECIDES TO FOCUS ON ONE THING. THAT
ONE EXACT THING THAT YOU HAVE
BEEN AVOIDING ALL DAY.

48

Goodbye sleep, hello 5am.

If you know someone who is getting bags under their eyes, let them know you are happy to listen to what keeps them awake until the dawn chorus each day. Whether they have a molehill or a mountain, a well-chosen one-liner can help them open up.

As they say, a problem shared is a problem halved. Just remember not to put the problem shared on Facebook.

PRIORITIES

**IF IT'S WORRYING, IT'S IMPORTANT.
BUT IS IT THAT IMPORTANT?**

- Don't sweat the petty things, and don't pet the sweaty things.

- Everything in life is temporary... So if things are going well, enjoy it, because it won't last forever. And if things are going badly, don't worry. It can't last forever either.

- In just two days, tomorrow will be yesterday.

- Just remember: if the world didn't suck, we'd all fall off.

- Don't take life too seriously; no one gets out alive.

- Keep hitting snooze until the real panic sets in.

TRUTH AND LIES

HONESTY IS OFTEN THE BEST POLICY.

- Your conscience is only clear if you don't use it.

- If you tell the truth you don't have to remember fictional details.

- A clear conscience is usually the sign of a bad memory.

- The best way to lie is to tell the truth. A carefully edited truth.

- A conscience is what hurts when all your other parts feel so good.

- Letting the cat out of the bag is a whole lot easier than putting it back in.

- Never admit or deny anything. It makes things more interesting.

- Never ask a barber if he thinks you need a haircut.

- Honesty is the best policy but insanity is the best defence.

LONG IN THE TOOTH

AT LEAST ANOTHER BIRTHDAY MEANS MORE CAKE.

- Age is just a number.

- We all spend our teens trying to appear older and the rest of our lives wanting to feel younger.

- Being 'over the hill' is much better than being under it.

- You are only young once, but you can be immature forever.

- Experience is something you don't get until just after you need it.

- We never really grow up, we only learn how to act in public.

- The older you get, the better you realise you were.

- Time is the best teacher; unfortunately it kills all of its students.

- Adults are just kids who owe money.

- Growing old is inevitable; growing up is optional.

- Birthdays are good for you. Statistics show that people who have the most live the longest.

- If you don't do stupid things while you're young, you'll have nothing to smile about when you're old.

- By the time you learn the rules of life, you're too old to play the game.

- There comes a time when you should stop expecting other people to make a big deal about your birthday. That time is: age 11.

A PROBLEM SHARED

JUST BETWEEN ME AND THE DOG. AND THE DOG DOESN'T EVEN HAVE A TWITTER ACCOUNT.

- I know you'd take my secrets to the grave.

- Don't worry, if my memory was any worse, I could plan my own surprise party.

- I'll keep your secrets under my hat if you do the same with that new haircut.

- Your secret is safe with me and my best friend.

- Your secrets are safe with me because I zone out every time you speak.

MONEY MONEY MONEY

RARELY FUNNY IN ANYONE'S WORLD.

- Living on earth may be expensive, but it includes an annual free trip around the sun.

- A bargain is something you don't need at a price you can't resist.

- Change is good, but £20 notes are better.

- Money talks. All it ever says is goodbye.

- Tip: borrow money from a pessimist, they don't expect it back.

- You have all the money you'll ever need. If you die by 4pm today.

- The best things in life are free, plus shipping and VAT.

- A fine is a tax for doing wrong. A tax is a fine for doing well.

- You're one step away from being filthy rich. All you need now is money.

- The Lottery is a tax on people who are bad at maths.

- The cost of living may be going up but it's still popular.

MONEY CAN'T
BUY HAPPINESS,
BUT IT CAN HELP
YOU LOOK FOR
IT FASTER, IN A
FANCY CAR.

PUT SOMETHING
ASIDE FOR A RAINY
DAY. AN UMBRELLA,
PERHAPS?

YOU NEED A NEW
BANK ACCOUNT
– YOUR LAST
ONE HAS RUN
OUT OF MONEY.

IF YOU THINK
YOU'RE HUNGRY,
YOU MIGHT JUST
BE THIRSTY. HAVE
A BOTTLE OF WINE
FIRST AND THEN
SEE HOW YOU FEEL.

YOU GET PLENTY OF
EXERCISE – JUMPING
TO CONCLUSIONS,
PUSHING YOUR
LUCK AND DODGING
DEADLINES.

56

KEEPING IN SHAPE

FIGHTING FIT OR FIGHTING AGAINST FITNESS?

- Eat well, stay fit, die anyway.

- Being a hypochondriac might save your life one of these days.

- Good health is merely the slowest possible rate at which one can die.

- Add squats to your workouts by moving the beer to the bottom of the fridge.

- You're not fat, you're just... easier to see.

- Exercise early in the morning before your brain figures out what you're doing.

- It's not a beer gut. It's a protective covering for your rock-hard abs.

- The more you weigh the harder you are to kidnap.

- Try to avoid things that make you look fat – like scales, mirrors and photographs.

- You're in shape. Round is a shape.

- A diet is a selection of food that makes other people lose weight.

- Red meat is not bad for you. Fuzzy green meat is bad for you.

GLASS
HALF EMPTY

FOR THOSE WHO MAKE WORRY A WAY OF LIFE.

- Worrying is like praying for what you don't want.

- Don't worry about the world ending today. It's most likely tomorrow in Australia already.

- Worrying is like a rocking chair: it gives you something to do, but doesn't get you anywhere.

- More people are killed by donkeys annually than are killed in plane crashes.

- Stop fighting your inner demons and get on the same side.

- It's bad luck to be superstitious.

- If you try to hold the weight of the world, I bet your knees break.

- Worrying works for me – 99% of the things I worry about never happen.

- Worrying will never change the outcome.

- Don't worry – just care and be prepared.

- Worrying is just betting against yourself.

GET
OVER IT

FOR EMERGENCY USE ONLY.

- It IS as bad as you think, and they ARE out to get you.

- Someday, we'll look back on this, laugh nervously, and change the subject.

- Stress is when you wake up screaming and you realise you haven't fallen asleep yet.

- If you can stay calm while all around you is chaos, then you probably haven't completely understood the situation.

- The deeper the pit you're falling into, the more chance you have to learn how to fly.

- Laugh at your problems, everybody else does.

- All of us have problems... it's just that some of us build a bridge and get over it.

- Don't suffer from insanity – enjoy every minute of it.

- Your life may not be working out, but everything else isn't that bad.

SECOND
THAT
EMOTION

NO MATTER WHAT PHONE
MANUFACTURERS SEEM TO THINK,
EMOTIONS AND FEELINGS ARE MORE
COMPLICATED THAN SIMPLE EMOJIS.

Say, for example, your friend's day started well with a great breakfast, but then they got a flat tyre, their boss cut their work hours, they found out their partner was cheating and then to round it off, their neighbour ran over their cat.

You won't display a huge amount of empathy by sending them a cartoon of a smiley poo, will you?

Even if the strength of the negative emotions seems to outweigh the cause, they are still valid to those going through them. Time to get the kettle on and dig out the biscuits. Not boring digestives. The proper biscuits.

ANGER MANAGEMENT

LET'S FACE IT, THE HULK IS NOT A GOOD LOOK.

- There's often a reason to be angry, but it's rarely a good one.

- If you let anger get the best of you, it can bring out the worst of you.

- Don't make them put 'What are you looking at?' on your headstone.

- If you are patient in one moment of anger, you will escape a hundred days of sorrow.

- Don't raise your voice, improve your argument.

- You look a little too short for your blood supply.

- Your problem isn't the problem. Your reaction is the problem.

- Treat anger like gold. Spend it wisely or not at all.

- Show a little bit of your anger every day instead of showing a lot of it on one day.

- Speak when you are angry and you'll make the best speech you'll ever regret.

- If a small thing makes you angry, what does it say about how big you are?

NO ONE
LIKES HATERS

**SOMETIMES THE BEST REVENGE IS
FORGIVENESS.**

- Hate is like swallowing poison and waiting for the other person to die.

- Half the people you hate don't care, and the other half don't know.

- Remember that you cannot hate someone you don't care about.

- As Mahatma Gandhi once said, 'Love the sinner but hate the sin.'

- Who needs enemies when you've got yourself?

- Hating people is like burning down your own house to get rid of a rat.

- Don't spend time hating people, spend time enjoying life when they aren't around.

- It's only when you throw someone off a cliff that you realise you want to rush to the bottom and catch them.

- Just imagine unplugging their life support machine to charge your phone and move on.

FEELING DOWN

IF YOU SMILED ALL THE TIME, PEOPLE WOULD THINK YOU WERE UP TO SOMETHING.

- At least today is another day that you aren't a dung beetle.

- Every day there's sad news and bad news, but each day itself is glad news.

- Don't ruin a good day thinking about a bad yesterday.

- You will never be truly happy if you keep holding on to things that make you sad.

- If you are in the wrong story, start a new one.

- Focus on the things you can change and let go of the things you can't.

- Waiting for someone else to make you happy is the best way to feel sad.

- Some days you have to create your own sunshine.

- Someone somewhere is having a worse day than you. And they might also live in Belgium. All. Year. Round.

TAKE A CHANCE

**THE ONLY THING TO FEAR IS FEAR ITSELF.
AND SPIDERS.**

- Life is not a dress rehearsal.

- This is your life, start living!

- If you're going to walk on thin ice, you may
  as well dance.

- If you keep your feet firmly on the ground,
  you'll have trouble putting on your pants.

- The things that come to those who wait
  are those things left by the ones who got
  there first.

- The only time the world beats a path to your
  door is if you're in the bathroom.

- You are the author of your own life. Start
  writing before your ink dries out.

GREEN-EYED MONSTER

A LOT OF EFFORT FOR SOMEONE ELSE'S GAIN.

- Just because you don't know about their problems doesn't mean they don't have any.

- Jealousy is the art of counting someone else's blessings instead of your own.

- You can't have everything. Where would you put it?

- Their life was a dream once too.

- When we're constantly wishing for something, we overlook everything we already have.

- If the grass is greener on the other side, you can bet the water bill is higher.

- Never trust a person who isn't having at least one crisis.

- Ignore the happy, smiling housewives on TV using a new cleaning product. Buy the pills they must be on instead.

- Never compare your life's journey with anyone else's. Your journey is your journey, not a competition.

THE GRASS IS ONLY GREENER ON THE OTHER SIDE BECAUSE THERE IS SO MUCH CRAP OVER THERE TO FERTILISE IT.

SOMETIMES YOU'RE AHEAD, SOMETIMES YOU'RE BEHIND.

SELF ESTEEM

BECAUSE IT'S NOT WHAT PEOPLE CALL YOU, IT'S WHAT YOU ANSWER TO.

- You are a nobody. Nobody is perfect. Therefore you are perfect.

- A diamond with a flaw is better than a common stone that is perfect.

- Your value doesn't decrease on someone's inability to see your worth.

- You don't need a certain number of friends, just a number of friends you can be certain of.

- Don't worry about those who talk behind your back. They are behind you for a reason.

- Don't feel bad. A lot of people have no talent.

- You are the best version of yourself, not a poor version of that idiot on the magazine cover.

- Some people come into your life as blessings and others come as life lessons.

- Don't give anyone permission to make you feel inferior.

- I have faith in fools – my friends call it self-confidence.

EVERYTHING CHANGES

THOSE WHO FEAR CHANGE CAN'T USE A VENDING MACHINE.

- Why is it new and improved? If it's new it's not an improvement of something, and if it's improved it can't be something new.

- If you do what you always did, you will get what you always got.

- Sometimes things fall apart so better things can fall into place.

- One of the fastest ways to improve your life is to simply do what you said you were going to do.

- The world changes so fast that the person who says it can't be done gets interrupted by the person who is already doing it.

- Say 'Yes' more often and life will return the favour.

- Never be afraid to try something new. Remember, amateurs built the ark, professionals built the *Titanic*.

EVERYTHING SUCKS

EVEN VACUUM CLEANERS.

- Don't let a bad day let you feel like you have a bad life.

- If we all threw our problems in a pile and we saw everyone else's, we'd grab ours back.

- If Lady Luck has turned her back on you, you can do whatever you want behind her back.

- Just when the caterpillar thought the world was ending, he turned into a butterfly.

- There is light at the end of the tunnel. Just be careful it's not a train.

- Good things are coming down the road. Just don't stop walking.

- There are no secret meetings. The world does not conspire against you. But you might not want to go to the village hall on Thursday evenings.

COMPLAINTS DEPARTMENT

A QUICK RANT HELPS LET OFF STEAM BUT PLEASE DON'T MAKE A HABIT OF IT.

- If you don't like something, change it. If you can't change it, change your attitude.

- Stop complaining. Everyone who died yesterday thinks you're one lucky SOB.

- If you can't see the bright side of life, polish the dull side.

- Count your rainbows, not your thunderstorms.

- Better to light a candle than to curse the darkness.

- If you're going through Hell, keep going.

- There's no point in crying over spilt milk. Unless it has coffee in it.

- I asked my North Korean friend how it was there, he said he couldn't complain.

- Spending today complaining about yesterday won't make tomorrow any better.

- Then again, if you can't repair your brakes, it can be worth making your horn louder.

THAT'S LIFE

NO ONE SAID LIFE WAS GOING TO BE EASY.
HOWEVER, A LOT OF PEOPLE HAVE SAID
'NO ONE SAID LIFE WAS GOING TO BE
EASY'. UNFORTUNATELY IT APPEARS
WE'VE FOUND THE CONSENSUS.

Tricky as life is, it doesn't come with an instruction book. So maybe each of us needs to write one of our own. And perhaps it could be kick-started with a few one-liners about life – though please consider the following lines as chapter headings rather than the full text or else your book won't be much of a read.

So get started, see it through to the end and measure your level of success. Or have a sandwich and a good think about it instead. We'll never know...

FIRST STEPS

PRACTICE MAKES PERFECT. JUST DON'T FORGET TO START PRACTISING.

- Yesterday you said tomorrow.

- Even if you're on the right track, you'll get run over if you just sit there.

- There are seven days in a week and 'someday' isn't one of them.

- Allow yourself to be the beginner. No one starts off excellent.

- Do not give up. The beginning is always the hardest.

- The best way to get something done is to begin.

- If your mind can conceive it, and your heart can believe it, you can achieve it!

- Don't compare someone else's middle to your beginning.

- Remember, Moses started out as a basket case.

- Stop wishing, start doing.

- If your ship doesn't come in, swim out to it.

- The journey of a thousand miles begins with a broken fan belt and a leaky tyre.

PUSHING THROUGH

WHEN THE GOING GETS TOUGH, CALL BILLY OCEAN.

- Remember: half the people you know are below average.

- Don't stress. Do your best. Forget the rest.

- Believe you can and you're halfway there.

- Keep repeating to yourself, 'Without ME, it's just AWESO'.

- A gem is not polished without rubbing, nor a man perfected without trials.

- Until you spread your wings, you'll have no idea how far you can fly.

- Whatever you do, always give 100%. Unless you are donating blood.

- When you feel like giving up, remember there are still a lot of MFs to prove wrong.

- With sufficient thrust, pigs fly just fine.

- When the world says 'give up', hope whispers 'try it one more time'.

- Bite off more than you can chew. Then chew like crazy.

THE MEANING OF LIFE

FYI – THIS ISN'T A SELF-HELP BOOK.

- When you get a handle on life, be careful not to break it.

- What screws us up the most in life is the picture in our head of how it is supposed to be.

- Unicorns are real, they're just fat and grey and we call them rhinos.

- Every time you find the meaning of life, they change it.

- Life is like a grammar lesson. You find the past perfect and the present tense.

- On the keyboard of life, always keep one finger on the escape key.

- Into every life some rain must fall. Usually when your car windows are down.

- You never really learn to swear until you learn to drive.

- The trouble with life is there's no background music.

- Life is only a comedy laid on for your personal amusement.

IF WINNING ISN'T EVERYTHING, WHY DO THEY KEEP SCORE?

LIFE IS ALL ABOUT PERSPECTIVE. THE SINKING OF THE *TITANIC* WAS A MIRACLE TO THE LOBSTERS IN THE SHIP'S KITCHEN.

I LOVE MY LIFE, BUT IT JUST WANTS TO BE FRIENDS...

OVERDOING IT

LET'S NOT TRY TOO HARD.

- Eagles may soar, but weasels don't get sucked into jet engines.

- Early to bed, early to rise, makes people suspicious.

- Ambition is a poor excuse for not having enough sense to be lazy.

- Consciousness: that annoying time between naps.

- Hard work has a future payoff. Laziness pays off now.

- Multitasking means screwing up several things at once.

- Progress is made by lazy men looking for an easier way to do things.

- Hard work never killed anyone, but why take the chance?

- The sooner you fall behind the more time you'll have to catch up.

- You can't fall off the floor.

UPS AND DOWNS

TAKING THE ROUGH WITH THE SMOOTH.

- Life is like toilet paper: you're either on a roll or taking crap from someone.

- Life is like a bird: it's pretty cute until it poops on your head.

- Life is like an onion: you peel it off one layer at a time, and sometimes you weep.

- Life is like a sewer: what you get out of it depends on what you put into it.

- Some days you are the fly, some days you are the windscreen.

- Some days you are the dog, some days you are the lamp post.

- Some days you are the pigeon, some days you are the statue.

- One day you're the best thing since sliced bread. The next, you're toast.

- On the other hand, you have different fingers.

TO ERR IS HUMAN

YOU LEARN FROM YOUR MISTAKES.
YOU WILL LEARN A LOT TODAY.

- A bad mistake becomes a good lesson if you choose to learn from it.

- Every morning is the dawn of a new error...

- Fall down seven times, get up eight.

- Every test in our life makes us bitter or better, every problem comes to make us or break us; our choice is whether we're the victim or victor.

- For maximum attention, nothing beats a good mistake.

- Good times become good memories and bad times become good lessons.

- Learn from your parents' mistakes: use birth control.

- Some mistakes are too much fun to only make once.

- Two wrongs are only the beginning.

- If you can smile when things go wrong, you have someone in mind to blame.

WHAT DOES SUCK SEED?

THIS IS THE FIFTH DRAFT OF THIS SECTION.

- If at first you don't succeed, blame someone else and seek counselling.

- If at first you don't succeed, destroy all evidence that you tried.

- If at first you don't succeed, we have a lot in common.

- If at first you don't succeed, change the rules.

- If at first you don't succeed, skydiving is not for you.

- Anyway, the road to success is often closed for resurfacing.

A CELEBRATION OF PROCRASTINATION

NEARLY DIDN'T WRITE THIS BIT.

- Plan to be spontaneous, tomorrow.

- Procrastination is the art of keeping up with yesterday.

- Keep the dream alive: hit the snooze button.

- Good things come to those that wait. Better things come to those that go out and get them.

- It's OK to take your foot off the pedal once in a while. Just don't pull into the layby forever.

- Tomorrow: the best labour-saving device of today.

- Do it tomorrow. You have made enough mistakes for today.

UNLUCKY DUCK

LUCK CAN BE THE ONLY EXPLANATION FOR EVERYONE ELSE'S SUCCESS.

- You'll never spot a four-leafed clover if you don't know how to count.

- Even a blind hog finds an acorn now and then.

- Luck is what you have left over after you give 100 per cent.

- The harder you work, the more luck you seem to have.

- You can always tell luck from ability by its duration.

- Racehorses have four bits of luck nailed to their feet, but they still get shot if they break a leg.

- It's bad luck to be superstitious.

- Life's a lottery you've already won – don't forget to cash in your ticket.

- That rabbit's foot didn't do so much for the rabbit.

DECORATIONS AND DISTRACTIONS

UNTIL NOW WE'VE BEEN PAIRING ONE-LINERS WITH SOME FAIRLY SPECIFIC MOMENTS IN LIFE. BUT IT'S NOT POSSIBLE TO PREPARE FOR EVERY EVENT OUR FAMILY MEMBERS, FRIENDS AND ACQUAINTANCES MAY GO THROUGH. IF YOU COULD FORESEE EVERYTHING, YOU'D STOP READING THIS BOOK AND BECOME A WEATHER FORECASTER/SUPERHERO.

Instead, let's end with a few general-purpose lines to help fill in the gaps. Those moments where someone needs a little lift or a distraction to take their mind off of things.

Clearly the best way to make someone feel positive about themselves is to give them a compliment. And what's better than that? A massive compliment. Better than that? OK... you get the idea.

And if you can't say something nice, wink, and say something a bit cheeky.

COMPLIMENTARY

INSTANT UPPERS FOR ALL OCCASIONS.

- Your smile is contagious.

- You look great today.

- You have the best laugh.

- You're strong.

- You have a great sense of humour.

- You are brave.

- You have the courage of your convictions.

- You're a great listener.

- You're wonderful.

- You're inspiring.

- You have the best ideas.

- You always know just what to say.

- You're great at figuring stuff out.

- You're so thoughtful.

- You seem to really know who you are.

REALLY COMPLIMENTARY

WHEN MORE THAN A LITTLE LIFT IS REQUIRED.

- You should be proud of yourself.

- That thing you don't like about yourself is what makes you so interesting.

- Jokes are funnier when you tell them.

- You always know how to find that silver lining.

- The people you love are lucky to have you in their lives.

- Your creative potential seems limitless.

- Any team would be lucky to have you on it.

- You're really something special.

- You're a gift to those around you.

REALLY, REALLY COMPLIMENTARY

TAKING BEING NICE TO A NEW LEVEL.

- Is that your picture next to 'charming' in the dictionary?
- On a scale from 1 to 10, you're an 11.
- There is ordinary and then there's you.
- I bet you sweat glitter.
- You were cool way before the hipsters.
- You're one of a kind.
- You could survive a Zombie apocalypse.
- You're more fun than bubble wrap.
- Who raised you? They deserve a medal for a job well done.

THANK YOU

SHOW YOUR APPRECIATION.

- You deserve a hug right now.
- You're more helpful than you realise.
- Being around you makes everything better!
- You should be thanked more often. So thank you!!
- Actions speak louder than words, and yours tell an incredible story.
- You light up the room.
- You bring out the best in other people.
- You always know – and say – exactly what I need to hear when I need to hear it.
- You're a candle in the darkness.
- You're a great example to others.
- Everything would be better if more people were like you!
- Being around you is like being on a happy little holiday.

WHY DOES SOMEONE BELIEVE YOU WHEN YOU SAY THERE ARE FOUR BILLION STARS, BUT HAVE TO CHECK WHEN YOU SAY THE PAINT IS WET?

DISTRACTION TECHNIQUE

IF IT'S ALL TOO MUCH, PONDER THE IMPONDERABLES.

- How do you tell when you run out of invisible ink?
- Should crematoria give discounts for burn victims?
- What happens if you get scared half to death twice?
- What if there were no hypothetical questions?
- What is a free gift? Aren't all gifts free?
- What's another word for Thesaurus?
- What's the speed of dark?
- Why is 'abbreviation' such a long word?
- Why is it called 'tourist season' if we can't shoot them?
- Why isn't 'phonetic' spelled the way it sounds?
- Why didn't Noah swat those two mosquitoes?
- Do fish get thirsty?
- Why is the day that you do laundry, cook, clean, iron and so on, called a day off?

TIPS AND TRICKS

TAKE MY ADVICE – I'M NOT USING IT.

- It's a small world. So don't worry about using your elbows a lot.

- Never, under any circumstances, take a sleeping pill and a laxative on the same night.

- When tempted to fight fire with fire, remember that the fire brigade usually uses water.

- Don't drink while driving – you'll spill the beer.

- If you go to sleep with a itching ass you will wake up with a stinking finger.

- Never do card tricks for the group you play poker with.

- Always take time to stop and smell the roses. Just be careful not to inhale a bee.

- Knowledge is power, and power corrupts. So study hard and be evil.

- If you have an open mind be careful your brains don't fall out.

- In case of fire, exit the building BEFORE tweeting about it.

- Improve your memory by doing unforgettable things.

WRITING. LIKE. THIS. DOESN'T. MAKE. YOUR. POINT. ANY. STRONGER.

I'VE LEARNED TWO IMPORTANT LESSONS IN LIFE. I FORGET THE FIRST ONE, BUT THE SECOND ONE IS TO WRITE THINGS DOWN.

WINNER
TAKES IT ALL

IF YOU WIN EVERY TIME IT GETS BORING.

- Find the key to success before someone changes the lock.

- A celebrity is someone who works hard to become known and then wears dark glasses to avoid being recognised.

- The trouble with doing something right the first time is that nobody appreciates how difficult it was.

- There are two rules for ultimate success in life. 1. Never tell everything you know.

- When everything's coming your way, you're on the wrong side of the road.

- The secret to success is to know who to blame for your failures.

- The early bird may get the worm, but the second mouse gets the cheese.

- To be sure of hitting the target, shoot first and call whatever you hit the target.

- If all else fails, lower your standards.